Agriculture in Virginia, 1607-1699

By

LYMAN CARRIER

Professor of Agriculture, Ferrum Junior College

VIRGINIA 350TH ANNIVERSARY CELEBRATION CORPORATION
WILLIAMSBURG, VIRGINIA
1957

36376
april 1958

Jamestown 350th Anniversary
Historical Booklet Number 14

Agriculture in Virginia, 1607-1699

Various events in the latter years of the sixteenth century did much to shape the future destiny of the English nation. With the destruction of the Spanish Armada in 1588, England rose from a minor position in world affairs to one of major importance. One of the first changes was reflected in her attitude towards trade and commerce. England was no longer penned up on her "tight little isle," and her ships could sail the high seas in comparative safety. Expansion of her foreign trade seemed the only answer to her ambitions, but foreign trade required a two way transfer of products. In order to sell goods, it was necessary to buy in exchange. World commerce had already become well stabilized among friendly nations making it difficult for outside businessmen to share in these established commitments. So England was soon to direct her attentions toward America.

It was with eyes focused on future trade that the businessmen who composed the London Company contributed the huge sums that were required to finance the settlement at Jamestown, Virginia. Agriculture was not of prime importance. At that time England was self-sufficient so far as the production of grains and livestock was concerned. Ordinary farm products would not pay the cost of transportation across the ocean. Of course, it was expected that the colonists would eventually produce their own food stuffs; however, until that stage of development occurred it was expected that the London Company would supply the needs of the colony direct from England.

The men of the first expedition were not farmers and took little interest in farming. A good many came, hoping to share in riches, that their imagination had created. Fantastic tales about the Americas had been circulated in Europe during the century following their discovery. The most authentic of these foreign

1

travel journals had been translated into English and published around the turn of the sixteenth century. Reports also of rich prizes, laden with gold, captured on the Spanish Main by English privateers, had inflamed the English mind. If the Spaniards could find such vast treasures in America, why should not the English do the same?

Then too, as the first colony of Virginia lay between 34 and 41 degrees north-latitude, the same approximately as Italy and Spain, it was expected that the much desired warm weather products enjoyed by the Mediterranean people, such as oranges, lemons, sugar, and spices could be produced equally as well in America. Jamestown eventually contributed great financial benefits to the Mother Country from agricultural accomplishments. These benefits could not in 1607 be visualized. To understand the vicissitudes which beset the colonists in the early years of the settlement, one should be familiar with the agricultural practices of both the Old World and the New, for it was by combining the farming wisdom of both sides of the Atlantic into a new agriculture, that the colony became firmly established.

OLD WORLD AGRICULTURE

European agriculture reached a high degree of efficiency two thousand years ago in the scrub-forest region around the Mediterranean Sea. To the Greeks that part of the world alone was considered fit for habitation by human beings. Farming by the Romans was regarded as a highly respectable and honorable occupation. Some of their most learned scholars wrote books on husbandry. The Romans have given us by far the most complete and satisfactory accounts of their agriculture of any ancient people. During the "Revival of Learning," these old masterpieces were rediscovered, constituting the principal agricultural literature of Europe, prior to the eighteenth century. Most of the early English books on husbandry were mere translations of the Roman books on that subject, with a few original observations added.

2

The northern or colder parts of Europe were many centuries behind the Mediterranean nations in agricultural achievement. At the time of the discovery of America, England and most of the nations of Europe were controlled by the feudal system. The arable land was owned in large estates or manors by feudal barons, the actual labor on the farms being performed by serfs. These farm laborers belonged to the land and were exchanged with it when there was a change in ownership of the real estate. Farming was looked upon as necessary to existence, but not as a business enterprise. Since trade and transportation in farm products were extremely limited, consumption took place near the fields of production. It was more economical for a baron to move his family and retinue of servants to different parts of his domain than it was to transport the food stuffs to one central habitation. The possibility of serfs becoming land owners was too remote for consideration.

CONTINENTAL INFLUENCES

Farming practices in England before the eighteenth century were largely adaptations from other European countries. The Romans, about the beginning of the Christian era, took their husbandry to the British Isles. The Anglo-Saxons in the fifth century, brought in from the mainland their farm practices. Likewise the Normans in the eleventh century brought over their methods of tillage. Owing to the close proximity to France, Flanders and Holland, agricultural innovations in those countries were not long in gaining attention and trial by the British farmers. The long hours of sunlight during short summers, with the opposite conditions prevailing in the winters, have influenced the development of plant species in all northern latitudes. Such seasonal conditions have also made necessary a distinct type of farming. Many crops of the Mediterranean region do not survive in north European countries. People in the colder regions also require a different diet than do those living in the warmer climates. By the seventeenth century an agriculture adapted to northern Europe had come into general practice. The implements used in farm work were, by modern standards, very crude and were customarily made by the local smith. A few hoes and mattocks, scythes, reaping hooks, spades and wooden plows with iron points and shares complete the list. The entire supply of tools for an average sized farm could have been hauled in one load on one of their two-wheeled carts.

CROPS GROWN

The chief grains of northern Europe were wheat, rye, oats, barley, and buckwheat. The common grasses, clover and turnips, were raised for forage. It should be noted that all of these crops were broad-cast seeded, none required row planting or intertillage.

A few American products had been brought to England prior to the settlement at Jamestown. They apparently came by the way of Asia. Maize was first called Turkey wheat. The great American bird was named Turkey. Thomas Tusser in 1573 in his "Five Hundred Pointes of Good Husbandrie" enumerates the meats suitable for a Christmas dinner with the following verse:

> "Beef, mutton and pork.
> Shred pies of the best
> Pig, veal, goose and capon
> And Turkey well drest."

No earlier mention of anything strictly American in English literature has come to light.

INDIAN AGRICULTURE

Let us turn now and take a look at the farming accomplishments of the American Indians. The oft repeated statement that the Indians lived mainly by hunting and fishing so far as it pertains to the Virginia tribes is far from the truth.

The bitter struggles between the white men and the Indians

during the colonial period created animosities and prejudices which have overshadowed the beneficial contributions the red men have made to civilization. As plant breeders, the American Indians rank with the most skillful of the world. Take for instance, maize or Indian corn. There is nothing closely comparable to it known to botanists. It has been domesticated so long that its wild prototype is unknown. Maize, now, could not exist anywhere in the world without the aid of man. The Indians had all the varieties that are now known, such as dent, flint, sweet, early, late, pop, and other special sorts which are no longer grown. They had developed varieties that matured all the way from the tropics to the St. Lawrence River in Canada.

The Indians also practiced a mixed culture such as corn, beans, and squashes all in the same hill; they had created a large number of varieties of beans (*Phaseolus genus*): the white, red, black, and spotted sorts now so commonly grown, and many others.

INDIAN TILLAGE

The Indians were able to clear fields, of several hundred acres in extent, without the aid of metal tools, using fire as their chief agent. Trees, too large to be cut with their stone hatchets, were killed either by building a fire at the base or by girdling the bark. The trees in dying furnished fire wood for domestic use. Planting began among the dead trees wherever enough loose dirt could be scraped together to make a hill for seeding. In the course of time the fields became entirely free from forest growth. These fields were cropped in most cases until their fertility was exhausted and then abandoned. If there was no more available fertile land in the vicinity, the tribe moved to a new location. The early white settlers on the Atlantic Coast found many of these abandoned clearings. Because of their unproductiveness they were called "poisoned fields."

The Indians had only the crudest sorts of farming tools. Near the coast, sea shells were the most efficient implements they possessed. The fresh-water clam-shells came next in usefulness. Where these natural scrapers were not available, pointed sticks, and pieces of flat rock served the purpose. One writer describing the Illinois Indians' method of farming says:

This tillage consists in breaking up just the surface of the earth with a sort of wooden instrument, like a little pickaxe, which they make by splitting the end of a thick piece of wood, that serves for a handle, and putting another piece of wood, sharp pointed at one end into the slit. This instrument serves them instead of a hoe or spade, for they have no iron tools.

INDIAN vs. OLD WORLD CULTURE

Attention has been called to the fact that all of the field crops of Great Britain, at the time of the English settlements in America, were broadcast seeded. The Indians had developed a far different cultural treatment for their crops. In their most common method, that of hill planting, the soil in the intervening spaces was not broken. The hills, two to four feet apart, were from 12 to 20 or more inches in diameter. The soil in these hills was all that was stirred or loosened. All weeds, both in the hills and the intervals between them, were kept cut or pulled out. Four to six grains of maize and two or three beans were seeded in each hill, separately spaced. Squashes and pumpkins were sometimes seeded with the corn and beans. This mixed seeding is a unique feature of American agriculture.

The Indians were fortunate in not having to contend with many of the weeds, insects and plant-diseases which now plague farmers and gardeners. Practically all of these pests, some of quite recent date, are of Old World origin and have been introduced by white men, into America.

Birds and small animals gave the Indians more concern than all their other pests combined. It was customary to build in their gardens small watch-houses in which the young folks took turns in staying to scare away crows and other troublesome birds.

The same hills were used year after year and became in time

quite sizable mounds, remains of which have persisted, in some localities, until modern times. In the southwestern parts of Michigan, the early settlers found large tracts of ridged land, evidently relics of Indian agriculture. It is now thought that these areas were corn fields in which the seeding was made in continuous rows instead of hills. A French artist in Florida in 1564 pictured the Indians seeding their crops in rows.

After a few years of failure in their attempts to grow American crops, the English colonists adopted the Indian method of seeding, but usually neglected the weeding, and were subjected to ridicule for their shiftlessness by the painstaking squaws. In using work-animals for cultivating corn, it was found advantageous to destroy the weeds by stirring the ground in the intervening spaces.

THE SETTLEMENT OF JAMESTOWN

On the 26th day of April, 1607, three small ships carrying 105 colonists passed between Cape Charles and Cape Henry into Chesapeake Bay for the purpose of founding a colony in the land called Virginia. The voyagers took seventeen days to investigate the advantages and disadvantages of that region for such an undertaking.

First consideration for selecting the site was its possibilities for defense against a foreign foe, especially the Spaniards, in Florida and the West Indies. This was no idle fear. Spain and England had for many years been in conflict. Moreover, Spain claimed all of the Americas by the right of discovery.

The second most important thing for consideration was adequate harbor facilities. In both of these particulars, the site selected about thirty miles up the James River left little to be desired. The Jamestown peninsula jutted out into the river far enough to give an unobstructed view for several miles. The character of the land on either side of the river would have made difficult any attempt at an overland attack.

The James was sufficiently deep to take care of any ocean going vessels of that time. The heavily forested surroundings furnished protection from violent storms. The channel ran near the shore. Ships could be moored by cables to trees on the land.

From the standpoint of raising food stuffs, the colonists could hardly have picked a more unfavorable situation. The peninsula was connected with the shore to the north by a narrow neck of land "thirty yards over." As this narrow strip of land was usually flooded during times of high water, the peninsula was for most purposes an island by which designation it is generally known.

There were about eight hundred and fifty acres of heavily timbered forest lands on the island and about eight hundred acres of marsh covered with coarse reedy grasses but there was no cleared land ready for seeding.

Clearing forest lands even with modern tools and equipment is a slow laborious process. Cutting down the trees is only a beginning. The stumps with their interlocking root systems have to be removed. It takes many years for hardwood stumps to rot to a condition that they may be easily destroyed. Although the trees on Jamestown Island were large, they could be cut, and those with straight grained boles rived into clapboards, or the logs rolled into piles and burned for their ashes, a product that was in demand in England for use in the manufacture of soap.

The soil on the Island may not have been very fertile. The fact that the Indians had never cleared any of the land indicates they did not consider it of the best quality.

First Attempts at Farming

Captain Newport assigned a third of the settlers, or about thirty-five men, to husbandry. Nothing came from their labors. At one of their first attempts to plant corn, probably English grain, they were assaulted by a few venturesome Indians which so discouraged the settlers, that they made no further efforts to provide crops for food that season. One of the colonists complained about the difficulties of preparing land for corn. Another mentions that some made gardens. The growing season was too far spent when they finally settled at Jamestown to allow for clearing land for spring-seeded grains.

By mid-summer their food supply was becoming seriously depleted. Fortunately the Indians remained friendly. Captain John Smith informs us that in July:

It pleased God to move the Indians to bring us corn ere it was halfe ripe to refresh us and in September they "brought us great store both of corne and bread ready made."

They had four acres of ground prepared the following year which they seeded to "corn" (wheat, barley or peas). No details are given except that nothing came from their efforts. Two growing seasons had passed and not a bushel of grain had been produced for their sustenance.

LIVESTOCK

Greater success came from their attempts to raise animals than attended their efforts to grow crops. A few animals were brought in. Reverend W. Simmonds states that: "three sowes in eighteene moneths, increased sixty and odd piggs. And neere 500 chickens brought up themselves without having any meat given them."

More livestock was evidently brought in the two supplies which arrived in 1608 as it was reported, at the time Smith left the colony in the fall of 1609, that they had "six mares and a horse; five or sixe hundred swine; as many hennes and chickens; some goats some sheepe." Captain John Smith during his two years with the colony was remarkably successful in obtaining from the Indians several hundred bushels of corn and beans in exchange for English manufactured goods. The fertile bottom lands of the rivers north of the James yielded bountiful harvests for the Indians as they have since for Virginians. Glass beads and tinkling bells intrigued the natives. The white man's clothing was also a source of wonderment. It was Smith's contention

9

that the white laborers should devote their time to getting out clapboards, pitch and soap-ashes to ship to England and depend on the Indians to keep the colony supplied with food. Smith was not a farmer. He little realized that the Indians' desire for trinkets would soon be satisfied. Then, too, public opinion in England, aroused by the Las Casas exposures of Spanish cruelties in the West Indies would not sanction forced enslavement of the natives. With the departure of Smith, in October, 1609, the lucrative Indian trade came to an end. No other member of the colony had the courage, for sometime, to visit the tribes along the York and Rappahannock rivers for the exchange of products.

First White Farmer in Virginia

The first experienced English farmer to come to the colony was William Spence, who arrived on the *Phoenix*, April 20, 1608. He was variously described as a laborer, gentleman, and ensign. Ralph Hamor certified to his character as "an honest, valiant, and industrious man." Spence survived the ordeals of the early years and was a member of the first House of Burgesses, in 1619. He probably lost his life in the Indian massacre of 1622. Five persons, names not given, were killed at that time on the Spence farm. Alexander Brown states that Ensign Spence is reported lost in 1623 but he may have been living in captivity.

It appears from this meager evidence that William Spence lived on his farm outside of the fortified area. If such were the case, he may have set a precedent that has had a pronounced influence on the development of this country. It was the belief of the authorities in the London Company that the colonists would all live in small communities for mutual protection and perform their tillage operations, if any, outside the settlement. These communities, sometimes under the name of "particular plantations" and sometimes "hundreds" were necessary in the early days. But from the beginning there were a few independent plantations, or farms, like that of William Spence. Mention has been made of the impossibility of a farm laborer in the Old Country ever attaining land ownership. But, here in America with its boundless acres, that great boon seemed within their reach. When allotments of land were finally made to individuals it was found advantageous for the owner to live on his farm rather than to operate it from a remote village. Freedom, independence, and the importance of the individual, which are characteristics of the American farmers, came into existence.

The common storehouse for provisions, tried at first in Jamestown, created friction and illwill and in a few years was abandoned. The members of the Council were accused of favoritism and self indulgence in using the food and other products in the storehouse. To have and to hold a parcel of land and to enjoy the fruits of one's own labors has been a compelling force in changing a wilderness into a mighty nation. That force had its inception in the infant colony at Jamestown.

A Change in Policy

The two years of failure to produce crops was convincing evidence that English methods of farming were not suited to Virginia conditions. The colonists were ready to try something else. They turned to the Indians to learn the secret of their successful farming operations.

A fortunate event occurred in the early spring of 1609. Two young Indians, by the names of Kemps and Tussore were taken prisoners in retaliation for the depredations of other Indians. At the time of their arrest they were described as "the two most exact villaines in the countrie, that would have betrayed both their king and kindred for a piece of copper." That this statement was not deserved was proven later. These two young Indians liked the Englishmen and the English way of living. It is also stated that while they were fettered prisoners they "did double taske and taught us how to order and plant our fields."

Food scarcity became in 1609 a serious problem. The eagerly

looked for supply ships from England did not come. To relieve the tension "Many were billetted among the salvages, whereby we knewe all their passages, fields and habitations; how to gather and use their fruits as well as themselves."

Kemps and Tussore were given their liberty soon after corn planting time. "But so well they liked our companies they did not desire to goe from us."

Nothing further is recorded as to the fate of Tussore, sometimes called Kinsock. Strachey, Secretary of the Colony who was in Virginia 1610-1611, mentions having obtained certain information from

One Kemps, an Indian, who died the last year of the scurvye at Jamestown, after he had dwelt with us almost one whole year, much made of by our lord generall and who could speake a pretty deale of English, and came orderly to church every day to prayers, and observed with us the keeping of the Sabaoth both by ceassing from labour and repairing to church.

STARVING TIME

Dire disaster finally struck the colony. Food supplies were exhausted. Starvation became a reality. A general drought blanketed eastern Virginia. The Indians too were on short rations. Smith, the provider, who had been injured by an explosion of gunpowder, had returned to England. It was one of the most cruel experiences ever endured by a group of men. The climax came during the winter of 1609-10.

A few quotations from the records of that period paint the picture in its most terrible colors. Lord De La Warr who arrived in 1610 just in time to save the colony from abandonment reported to the London Company:

Our people, together with the Indians (not to friend), had the last winter destroyed and kild up all our hoggs, insomuch as of five or six hundred (as it is supposed), there was not above one sow, that we can heare of, left alive; not a henn nor a chick in the forte (and our horses and mares they had eaten with the first).

12

A
NEW INSTVCTION
OF PLOWING AND SET-
TING OF CORNE, HANDLED
IN MANNER OF A DIALOGVE
betweene a Ploughman and a
Scholler.

Wherein is proued plainely that Plowing and
Setting, is much more profitable and leſſe
chargeable, than Plowing and
Sowing.

By Edvvard Maxey. Gent.

*He that withdraweth the Corne, the people will curſe him: but bleſſing
ſhall be vpon the head of him that ſelleth Corne.* Prou.11.26.

Imprinted at London by *Felix Kyngſton*, dwelling in Pater
noſter Rowe, ouer againſt the ſigne of the
Checker. 1601.

Indians boiling maple sap below and planting corn above.

Picture by Lafitau, 1724.

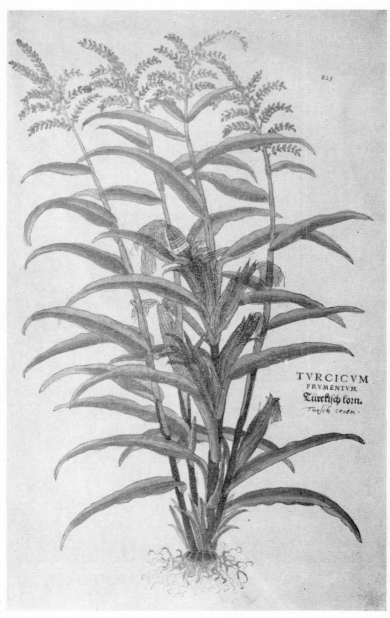

815

TVRCICVM
FRVMENTVM
Türckisch korn.
Turfch coren.

The earliest picture of Maize.

Copied from Leonhard Fuchs 1542.

And Reverend William Simmonds states in regard to this same starving time of the winter of 1609-10:

> as for our hogs, hens, goats, sheepe, horse, or what lived; our commanders and officers did daily consume them: some small proportions (sometimes) we tasted, till all was devoured.

Thus after three years they had nothing of a material nature to show for their efforts. Their most valuable achievement had been their acquired knowledge of the Indians' methods of farming. To make a bad situation worse the Indians began to make trouble. Lord De La Warr speaks of their "late injuries and murthering of our men." It was not until 1611 that real farming got under way at Jamestown. Then corn planting and fence building began in earnest.

Governor Dale Takes Charge

Sir Thomas Dale with "three ships, men, and cattell (100 kine, 200 swine)" arrived in Virginia May 10, 1611. Dale had seen military service in the Old World and was a severe and strict disciplinarian. The surviving colonists received a jolt in their manner of living. From habits of indolence into which they had fallen, owing to the hot climate and lack of food, after the departure of Captain John Smith, they were with little ceremony put to work. "His first care therefore was to imploy all hands in the setting of corne at the two forts at Kecoughtan, Henry and Charles," wrote Ralph Hamor "and about the end of May wee had an indifferent crop of good corne." This corn was planted near what is now Hampton where Strachey says, "so much ground is there cleared and open; enough with little labour already prepared to receive corne or make viniards of two or three thowsand acres." With corn planting completed, two palisaded forts were built for the protection of a few men left to care for the crops. They made another planting across Chesapeake Bay on the Virginia Cape. They had learned the hard way that clearing the heavily timbered land at Jamestown was hopeless for

13

immediate results. Dale then returned to Jamestown "where the most companie were, and their daily and usual works, bowling in the streets." This game was interrupted and the men put to work felling timber, repairing their houses and providing pointed pickets for fencing a new town, which Dale proposed to build, eighty miles above Jamestown.

HENRICO SETTLED

In August, 1611, Sir Thomas Gates arrived with "six tall ships with three hundred men, and one hundred kine and other cattel." Gates thoroughly approved of Dale's plans and policies and let him select about three hundred of the best workers in the colony to build at Henrico, now Farrar's Island, at Dutch Gap.

Within ten or twelve daies he had invironed it with a pale, and in honour of our noble Prince *Henry*, called it *Henrico*. The next worke he did, was building at each corner of the towne a high commanding watch-house, a church, and store-houses: which finished, hee began to thinke upon convenient houses for himselfe and men, which, with all possible speed hee could, he effected to the great content of his companie, and all the colonie.

This towne is situated upon a necke of a plaine rising land, three parts invironed with the maine river, the necke of land well impaled, makes it like an ile; it hath three streets of well framed houses, a handsome church, and the foundation of a better laid (to bee built of bricke), besides store-houses, watch-houses, and such like. Upon the verge of the river there are five houses, within live the honester sort of people, as farmers in England, and they keepe continuall centinell for the townes securitie.

About two miles from the towne, into the maine, is another pale, neere two miles in length, from river to river, guarded with severall commanders, with a good quantitie, of corne-ground impaled, sufficiently secured to maintaine more than I suppose will come this three yeeres.

APPOMATTOX LANDS SEIZED

The Appomattox Indians, at the time of the Jamestown settlement, were located on a neck of land lying between the James

14

and Appomattox Rivers. Dale wanted this land. It was cleared, fertile, and easy to fence, so we are told:

About Christmas following in this same year 1611 in regard of the injury done us . . . without the losse of any except some few salvages tooke it and their corne.

This newly acquired land he named New Bermudas and he divided it into several tracts known as "hundreds." The term hundred was a relic of the feudal system. It meant a political subdivision smaller than a county. It appears to have been Dale's intention that these hundreds or group plantations, often referred to as "particular plantations," should include the land that could be worked conveniently by the farmers from their homes in a village or a town. This plan was not popular. As has been previously stated the colonial pioneers much preferred to live on the land they tilled. The term "hundred" lost its significance.

Ralph Hamor described the operations at New Bermudas in the following:

In the nether hundred he [Dale] first began to plant, for there is the most corne-ground and with a pale of two miles cut over from river to river, whereby we have secured eight English miles in compasse. . . . Rochdale, by a crosse pale wel nigh foure miles long, is also planted with houses along the pale, in which hundred our hogs and cattell have twentie miles circuit to graze in securely.

Outstanding were the accomplishments of this taskmaster, Governor Dale, in one year, with men many of whom were unaccustomed to manual labor. While some were engaged in fence building and the construction of houses, others were employed in getting out clapboards. Still others were gathering pitch and tar from the pine trees and burning logs to make soap-ashes. The London Company had incurred heavy expense in the settlement and was asking for something in return. Products from the forests were all that were available. It is no wonder that the colonists complained bitterly about their hardships in their letters to the folks back home.

It was not Gov. Dale's purpose to develop an agricultural colony. Surplus from food products would not pay the cost of shipment across the ocean. His plantings of corn were purely for local consumption. He limited the number engaged in farming, and to each of those so engaged, he allotted three acres of corn land. These farmers were not allowed to devote their entire time to crop-raising. The livestock as we have seen was allowed to run at large in the fenced ranges. In a letter dated June 14, 1614, Gov. Dale reported that he had set the colonists to the task of "husbanding our corne securely, whereof wee have above five-hundred acres set, and God be praised in more forwardness than any of the Indians that I have seen or heard of this yeare."

When Capt. Argall, as deputy governor superseded Dale in May, 1617, George Yeardley having been acting governor from April 11, 1616, he reported that the colony had about four hundred people but not over 200 fit for husbandry and tillage. As for livestock, they had 128 cattle, 88 goats, and a large number of hogs. As to cattle there were about "fortie bulls and oxen but they wanted men to bring them to labour and irons for the ploughs and harnesse for the cattell." They had tried again to grow some small grains.

Thirtie or fortie acres wee had sowne with one plough, but it stood so long on the ground before it was reaped it was most shaken.

This was a pitiful showing for the ten years that had elapsed since Capt. Newport established the colony. It had been a decade of frustration and heart-breaking disappointments, a decade of gruelling toil and misery. No blame should be attached to the colonists. They were thrust into a situation for which they were woefully unprepared.

The Dawn of Better Times

Virginia was destined to develop agriculturally. Attempts to suppress that industry only served to prolong the colony's troubles. There were no natural resources except the forests in the tidewater region; no Indian trade of any great value; no gems to be picked up at will; no minerals to be exploited. When the situation seemed most hopeless, the culture of a crop new to English farming completely changed their mental and pecuniary outlook. Despair changed to violent optimism. John Rolfe is generally credited with having been, in 1612, the first Virginia planter to engage in the growing of tobacco. Governor Dale at the time frowned on its culture and ruled that two of each man's allotment of three acres of land should be seeded to corn. Hence the change in governorship was a momentous event.

Change in Policy

When Sir Thomas Dale left, in 1616, George Yeardley took over the management of the colony as Acting Governor. He lost no time in putting an end to the restrictions on tobacco culture. The next year, 1617, saw a remarkable transformation in the colonists' way of life. Inertia gave way to frantic activity. "The market-place and streets and all other spare places were set with the crop and the colonie dispersed all about planting tobacco." Nor is this surprising. Tobacco alone promised them surcease from poverty and want. Hope for a bountiful harvest spurred them on as it has spurred farmers in all generations.

Tobacco in England

Many fantastic tales have been written about the introduction of the use of tobacco in England. Some of the most authentic historical items follow: The Spaniards found the natives in the West Indies using the plant both for chewing and smoking. They took seed to Europe where its use soon spread to other countries around the Mediterranean Sea.

The first Englishman to report on the addiction of the American Indians to the use of tobacco appears to have been John Sparke who wrote the account of the voyage of Sir John Hawkins who, in the course of his travels, spent some months, in 1565, with an ill-fated French colony in Florida. Sparke reported "The Floridians when they travell, have a kinde of herbe dried, who with a cane and an earthen cup in the end, with fire, and the dried herbs put together, doe sucke thorow the cane the smoke thereof, which smoke satisfieth their hunger, and therewith they live foure or five dayes without meat or drinke, and this the Frenchmen used for this purpose." It is quite likely that the sailors under Hawkins command acquired the habit and took some of the "dried herbs" back to England.

Sir Walter Raleigh is often credited with the introduction of the use of tobacco in England. While he may not have been responsible for its introduction, he apparently played an important role in the spread of the tobacco habit among the English aristocracy. Raleigh's interest in tobacco was no doubt aroused by the report of his protégé, the famous sixteenth century mathematician, Thomas Hariot. Hariot spent a year, June, 1585-June, 1586, with the Raleigh Colony on Roanoke Island. On his return to England he reported on the Indians' farming operations in Eastern North Carolina. For tobacco he wrote in part "We ourselves, during the time we were there, used to sucke it after their manner, as also since our returne, and have found many rare and wonderful experiments of the virtues thereof, of which the relation would require a volume by itselfe: the use of it by so many, of late, men and women of great calling, as els, and some physicians also, is sufficient witnesse."

Raleigh later made a voyage to the Island of Trinidad and the Orinoco River in South America from whence had come the most desirable sorts. Spain and Portugal monopolized the European tobacco trade with these mild varieties since the tobacco grown by the Virginia Indians had a sharp, biting taste. Plantings of these better sorts were made in England. A violent controversy was soon raging. King James I who detested Raleigh and all his activities, issued a *Counter Blaste* against tobacco. This was a most bitter tirade as the following quotation shows:

A custom loathsome to the eye, hateful to the nose, harmful to the brain, dangerous to the lungs, and in the black stinking fume thereof nearest resembling the stygian smoke of the pit that is bottomless.

Since the days of King James, millions of words have been written condemning the use of the "tawny weed."

The opposition of King James to tobacco led to the imposition of taxes on its import into England: that from Spain and Portugal was 2d a pound; that from Virginia 6s. 10d. In spite of all this array of evidence as to the detrimental effects of tobacco on the human body its consumption has steadily increased and spread over the entire world. Colossal fortunes have been made in its processing and trade. No product of the soil with the exception of grains used in the manufacture of alcoholic beverages has ever returned such bounteous revenues to the United States government. In the fiscal year ending June 30, 1954 there was paid into the treasury of the United States, the gigantic sum of $1,580,-299,000 from taxes on various tobacco products. Of this vast total, Virginia tobacco manufacturers that year contributed 356,-867,000 dollars. Municipal and other local taxes are not included in these figures.

Tobacco culture in America was a highly profitable enterprise for England. The colonists produced and sold the raw product. Very little tobacco is used in the raw state. Before tobacco is ready for the market it must be processed into the various forms demanded by the trade. It was estimated that one man engaged in tobacco growing in Virginia kept three Englishmen employed, that is, sailors engaged in transportation, processors and tradesmen. The English government also derived considerable revenue on the surplus tobacco products resold on the European market.

Tobacco Became Money

One of the needs of the colony was a medium of exchange: something that could be used for money. As the balance of trade was heavily in favor of the Mother Country, there was no opportunity for an accumulation of English money in America. So tobacco became acceptable for goods, services, and the payment of debts. Salaries were fixed in pounds of tobacco.

Fluctuating Prices

The value placed on tobacco in England varied with the supply and demand. With the introduction of Negroes in 1619, and the greatly increased immigration from England, the acreage devoted to the culture of tobacco expanded rapidly. The first serious effects of over-production occurred in 1630, when the price fell from three shillings, six pence to one penny a pound. This calamity proved to be a blessing in disguise. The next year, a boat of "18 tons burden," loaded with corn and tobacco disposed of its cargo at Salem, Massachusetts, then but recently settled. The corn brought six shillings a bushel. This started a brisk trade and a Dutch ship, in 1632, took 2,000 bushels of corn from Virginia to New England. In 1633, it was estimated that 10,000 bushels of corn from Virginia were sold in Massachusetts besides a number of beef cattle, goats, and hogs. In spite of the ruinously low prices which sometimes prevailed, the amount of tobacco shipped overseas continued to increase. In 1639, 1,500,000 pounds were exported from Virginia alone.

Growth of the Colony

Captain John Smith summarized the condition of the colony in 1629 in these words:

Master Hutchins saith, they have 2,000 cattle, and about 5,000 people; but Master Floud, John Davis, William Emerson, and divers others, say about five thousand people, and five thousand kine, calves, oxen, and bulls; for goats, hogs, and poultry; corne, fish, deere, and many sorts of other wild beasts; and fowle in their season, they have so much more than they spend, they are able to feed three or foure hundred men more than they have.

Starving times as a rule were over. Periods of short rations occurred infrequently and then only in times of disaster such as the aftermath of the Indian massacre of 1622 or when the planters became so engrossed in growing tobacco that they neglected to plant maize or other grains. Each succeeding crop was new wealth, something that had not existed before. Gradually, harvest after harvest, the colonists were able to add to their possessions additional tools and equipment.

He was a shiftless man indeed who could not provide ample food for his own needs. The history of Virginia during colonial times was intimately connected with the tobacco crop. The general welfare of the people rose and fell with the value placed on the leaf in England.

Efforts to Sustain Higher Prices

With the over supply of tobacco the English market became extremely discriminating in regard to the quality of the leaf it would purchase. The colonial government from time to time resorted to legislative expedients to prevent the shipment of inferior grades. Governor Wyatt, in 1621 ordered that "for every head they should plant but 1,000 plants of tobacco and upon each plant nine leaves." John Rolfe also stated, in 1619, that, "An industrious man not otherwaies imploied may well tend foure akers of corne, and 1,000 plants of tobacco." A thousand plants would give each worker about 112 pounds of tobacco a year. In 1628, an inspection law was enacted and in 1640, it was ordered that all bad tobacco and half the good should be destroyed.

Governor Berkeley, in 1664, made several ineffectual attempts to form agreements, with the planters of Maryland and North Carolina, to restrict the production of tobacco. The planters of each colony were willing for those of the other to stop planting, or to destroy as much tobacco as they pleased; but looking to their own selfish interests they would increase rather than decrease their crop. The Virginia General Assembly, in 1666, prohibited all culture of tobacco but the Maryland authorities complained that the law was ignored by the Virginia planters.

The Virginia colonists developed a keen rivalry among themselves in efforts to improve the quality of the leaf grown. Reverend John Clayton, in 1688, says: "For there is not only two distinct sorts of sweet-scented and Aranoko tobacco but of these be several sorts, much different, the seeds whereof are known by distinct names, of those gentlemen most famed for such sort of tobacco, as of prior seed etc."

The Aranoko, probably from the Orinoco river region in South America, was grown on the heavy clay soils. The product was a strong tobacco that was most in demand in Germany and other North European countries. The sweet-scented was grown on the lighter sandy soils and although the yield was less it brought a better price on the market. Hugh Jones, in his *Present State of Virginia*, in 1724, mentions one of the many localities in Virginia which became noted for a particular variety of tobacco grown there. To quote: "For on York River in a small tract of land called Digges Neck, which is poorer than a great deal of other land in the same latitude, by a particular seed and management, is made the famous crop known by the name of E Dees, remarkable for its mild taste and fine smell."

Topping the growing tobacco plants was a practice originated by the colonists. The main purpose was to limit the production to the large lower leaves and to do away with the small immature leaves at the top of the stem. The General Assembly often specified the number of leaves which could be left; the number, varying with the value placed on the leaf in England, ranged usually from six to nine.

Tobacco is a soil exhausting crop. The Jamestown planters

soon learned that continuous crops of tobacco, on the same land, soon reduced both the quantity and quality of the leaf. The only resource left to the tobacco farmers was to clear new fields. The more well-to-do planters began to seek favorable locations of uncleared land. The depleted fields were abandoned and the task of restoring their productivity was usually left to nature. Much of the best tobacco soils of Virginia have been cropped and then allowed to go back to brush and trees and again cleared several times. Finding the remains of old tobacco rows out in dense woods is not an uncommon experience. This exhaustion of tobacco lands had a beneficial influence on the agricultural development of Virginia. By the time the fields were abandoned, most of the stumps had decayed and the soil could be prepared for seeding to other crops with plow and harrows. It was found that these depleted fields were still capable of producing satisfactory crops of grain. Many of the colonists who were not financially able to clear new grounds could often buy or rent these abandoned fields for a nominal price.

Crops Other Than Tobacco

While tobacco played a very important part in building a prosperous colony at Jamestown, there were several other staples that also contributed to this result. Of prime importance should be rated maize or Indian Corn. Maize saved the colony from starvation on several occasions. Maize became an export commodity to the New England and West Indian colonies when the price for tobacco fell below the cost of transportation to Europe. Maize aided the colonists in the production of valuable livestock products. This crop has done more to promote the wealth and welfare of this country than all the natural resources, water-power, and forests put together. In order to increase the production of grain in 1623, the General Assembly ordered: "For the encouragement of men to plant store of corne, the prise shall not be stinted but it shall be free for every man to sell it as deere as he can." This law had a wholesome effect. It so increased the production of maize that seven years later as has already been noted, the colonists had a surplus of this product to export to New England. This is perhaps the first law passed in America for the direct benefit of the producers. It stands out in strong contrast to some legislative enactments. There were many other grain laws put on the statute books but the majority of them either fixed the maximum price for which the grain could be sold or else prohibited its exportation. The authorities in England were continually clamoring for products to supplement the tobacco exports.

Until 1685, each succeeding Governor as he sailed to Virginia was instructed to "use every means in his power to encourage the production of silk, wine, hemp, flax, pitch and potashes." The reason for finally omitting this clause is interesting. The King was concerned about the revenue the government was deriving from tobacco and did not wish for the colonists to engage in any enterprise that might diminish the volume of leaf that was coming to England. The omission of this clause marked a new era in the relation of the colony to the Mother Country. During the sixty years the clause was in force, several Governors, notably Wyatt, Harvey and Berkeley, had tried to comply with the wishes of the authorities in England, with extremely meager results to show for their efforts.

SILK CULTURE

There is very little justification for including silk culture as an enterprise in the agricultural history of the Jamestown Colony. It was one product that was usually placed first in recommendations of the authorities who sponsored the settlement of Virginia.

In keeping with the improved status of the social and economic life of England, in the latter years of the sixteenth century, came a desire for finer and more lustrous fabrics in their articles of dress. Serges and tweeds, woven from the fleeces of their coarse-wooled sheep, no longer satisfied the fastidious tastes of the ruling aristocracy. Even calicos from far-away Calcutta were esteemed fit for royal inaugural gowns. Silk was the last word in luxurious garb.

Silkworms had been reared in the Orient from ancient times. These moths had been domesticated for so many years they had become fully dependent on human aid for existence. They could crawl but could not fly. While silk brought fabulous prices on the world's market there were numerous reasons why its culture never succeeded in America. The handling of the creeping, crawling, ill-smelling worms was objectionable to anyone not accustomed from childhood to the task. Old people and young girls who were the ones employed in rearing silkworms in the Orient received the equivalent of a few cents a day for their labor. Such cheap help was not available in Virginia. Perhaps, the most serious objection of all was the lack of a suitable food supply for the worms. A silkworm from the time it hatches from the egg till it spins its cocoon devours a mass of green forage. Leaves of the mulberry tree are its favorite diet. In fact, without a supply of mulberry trees, successful silk culture is out of the question. Growing a crop of trees had to precede the rearing of worms. This took several years. Nevertheless, the directions of the London Company urged in season and out that the colonists should produce silk.

Governor Wyatt, in 1621, was instructed: "Not to permit any, but the council and heads of hundreds, to wear gold in the clothes, or to wear silk till they make it themselves." Nothing came from this order. In 1656, the agitation for silk became so intense, the General Assembly was forced to take action. First, an experienced silk grower, an Armenian by the name of George, was sent to the colony, and the General Assembly was ordered to give him four thousand pounds of tobacco to keep him in the country. Another law, passed that year, ordered that each planter set out ten mulberry trees for each one hundred acres

25

of land he owned. These trees were to be fenced, to protect them from horses and cattle, and to be kept weeded. This law was repealed, two years later, as it "seems rather troublesome and burthensome than any waies advantageous to the country." The law was re-enacted in 1661 but given a three years delay as it was impossible to get mulberry trees. The General Assembly, in 1657, voted a bounty of 5000 pounds of tobacco to any planter producing 100 pounds of wound silk. There were no claimants. Two years later, the bounty was increased to 10,000 pounds of tobacco and the amount of silk required was reduced to 50 pounds. Again the results were negative. Then a bounty of fifty pounds of tobacco for each pound of silk was ordered. The effects from all these orders are summed up in an act of the General Assembly in 1663 which reads:

George, the Armenian, having proved the making of ten pounds of wound silk, it is ordered there be paid him for his encouragement in the levy according to act.

It is assumed that George received 500 pounds of tobacco. What became of the silk is not recorded. A few years later the price per pound of wound silk was fixed by the General Assembly at 20 shillings or two hundred pounds of tobacco.

HEMP AND FLAX

Two plants, the culture of which was strongly urged by the English authorities, were hemp and flax. In this case, greater success was realized than occurred with most of the demands that came from across the ocean. It had been ordered in 1658, by the General Assembly: "That what person or persons, soever, shall at any time hereafter make, in this colonie, so much silke, flax, hopps or any other staple commodities (except tobacco) as is worth two hundred pounds sterling, or English wheate to the value of five hundred pounds stirling in one yeare, and exporte the same or cause the same to be exported, or shall first make two tunne of wine raized out of a vineyard made in this collonie, shall have given him by this country, for an encouragement, ten thousand pounds of Virginia tobacco."

Apparently no one qualified for the bounty on flax for, in 1661, provision was made for importing some flax seed from England. No price was fixed, in 1666, on "flax by reason of the uncertainty of the quality." In 1682, bounties were offered: "For every peck of flax seeds, four and twentie pounds of tobacco, and for every peck of hemp seed twenty pounds of tobacco." Bounties were also offered for hemp and flax woven into cloth. It was also ordered that every tithable person should produce one pound of dressed hemp and one pound of dressed flax or two pounds of either annually. From that time on considerable hemp and flax were raised in Virginia, but most of the crop was used at home. Linen cloth was highly prized. There was also a demand for cordage made of hemp fibers for ships.

English Grain

As already noted, the initial attempts of the colonists to grow the grains with which they had been accustomed in England came to naught. They were familiar with wheat, rye, barley and oats. To make satisfactory yields, these grains had to be broadcasted on well prepared seed beds. Newly cleared forests left the soil full of stumps and roots. The wooden plows of those days were useless on these newly cleared lands. Preparation of the soil, for tobacco or maize, could be accomplished with a hand hoe or shovel. These plants required space in which to develop their full growth. A tobacco plant could be set or a hill of corn planted wherever a little loose dirt could be found. Some English grains were seeded in the cleared land near Hampton and Newport News but these old fields, abandoned by the Indians, were also near to exhaustion. An "indifferent crop" was reported.

In 1627, Abraham Piersey had 200 acres each in wheat and

barley. From these crops he was able to furnish food daily to sixty persons. How much of this seeding was on land that had been abandoned for tobacco, or was old Indian fields, is not stated. When DeVries visited Virginia in 1643, he found the planters putting down, in English grain, lands which had been exhausted by successive crops of tobacco. The General Assembly had ruled in 1639, that corn (probably wheat and maize) could be exported whenever the price fell below twelve shillings a bushel. Large exports of this valuable cereal were then being made to the near-by colonies of Maryland, Manhattan, Carolina and the West Indies.

It was estimated by Edward Williams, in 1650, that two able-bodied laborers could seed sixty acres in wheat in the course of one season and reap the grain when it was ripe. The yield from such an area had a market value of four hundred and eighty pounds sterling. It was reported that these fields which no longer produced the best grades of tobacco were better for wheat than newly cleared land. As these exhausted fields could be rented or purchased at moderate cost compared with prime tobacco new ground, many poorly financed colonists were able to get a start towards prosperity without resorting to the almost universal practice of growing tobacco.

LIVESTOCK

As already shown, the domestic animals brought to the Colony, in the first few years of its settlement, were turned out in the woods to fend for themselves. The original breeding stocks were of ordinary quality and the lack of care given them contributed to their inferiority. Predatory animals such as wolves, bears, panthers and wild cats exacted a heavy annual toll of young animals.

Until Governor Dale constructed his miles of picket fences there was nothing to keep the animals from wandering up into the highlands where the colonists did not dare to venture. In

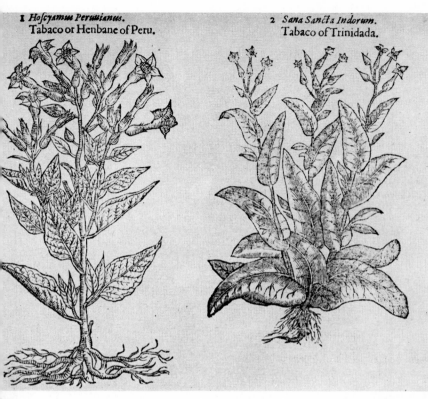

1 *Hofcyamus Peruuianus.*
Tabaco or Henbane of Peru.

2 *Sana Sancta Indorum.*
Tabaco of Trinidada.

Two varieties of tobacco as pictured by Gerard in 1597. The seeds of these two varieties were taken to Virginia by the Jamestown Settlers.

The Trenching gouge to be vſed as the Spade

The Turving Spade

The Trenching Spade

pag: 69

The paring Spade

The Trenching Wheele plough

The plaine Trenching Plough

Pag: 67

The Single Wheele plough

The Trenching Spade Cutting it's trench & the Water Following

Trenching Implements, Seventeenth Century

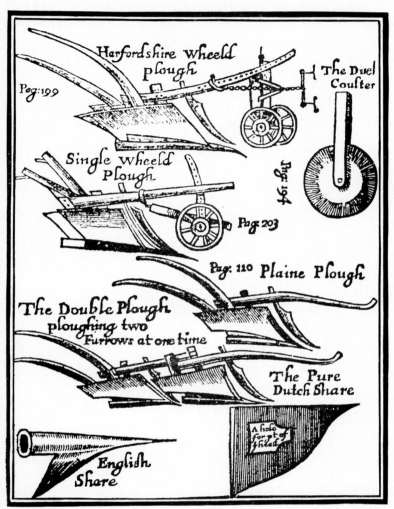

Harfordshire Wheeld plough

Pag:199

The Duel Coulter

Single Wheeld Plough.

Pag: 194

Pag: 203

Pag: 110 Plaine Plough

The Double Plough ploughing two Furrows at one time

The Pure Dutch Share

A hole for the Shlad

English Share

Seventeenth Century Plows

spite of the handicaps all classes of domestic animals increased in numbers when not slaughtered for food. This was especially true of swine.

SWINE

Hogs contributed more to the material welfare of the Jamestown Colony than historians have generally recognized. Hogs have many advantages over other breeds of livestock. They multiply much faster than any other domestic animal except poultry. They make faster gains and double the weight for the food consumed than do cattle, sheep or goats. When slaughtered, hogs dress out about 75 percent edible meat, as compared with 55 to 60 percent for cattle. When given wide open range in humid climates such as prevailed in the Tidewater, they do fairly well without other feed than what they can find for themselves.

In summer, at Jamestown, they obtained most of their living in the numerous fresh-water swamps. Tuckahoe, a flag-like swamp plant, with an enormous root system, was their favorite hot weather forage. The roots of tuckahoe, often as large as a man's arm, contain a crystalline acid that burns the mouth of a human being like fire. After a few trials, hogs seem to relish it. While tuckahoe is not a fattening feed, hogs eating it make satisfactory gains in weight.

In the fall when the acorns and nuts ripened, the hogs put on weight at a rapid pace. The woods were stocked with oak, hickory, chestnut, beech, chinquapin, and persimmon trees and shrubs, the fruits of which were all grouped under the general term *mast*. There is one difference between pork produced from grain-fed hogs and those fattened on mast. The lard of the latter group melts at a temperature of about ten degrees below that of those fed corn. To the connoisseur of well cured hams and bacon this low melting point is not a detriment but a distinct improvement.

The colonists adapted the Indian practice of using smoke to

aid in the curing of meat. The natives built platforms of poles supported by posts about six feet from the ground. The meat to be cured was salted and spread on these poles. A small fire was built underneath to furnish the smoke. This arrangement was called by the Taino Indians, a *barbacoa* from which we get the English equivalent, *barbecue*.

By 1636, hogs, sheep and goats had increased in such numbers that ships coming to Jamestown could supply their needs for meat from the colony's surplus. This was advantageous to shipmasters and furnished a market for a product of a growing industry in the colony. Prior to that time ships coming to America from Europe had to take on food stuffs for the round trip.

Another benefit accrued to the colony. The combined curing process of salt and smoke imparts a delicious flavor to hams and bacon that has never been excelled by any other method. This applies especially to meat from hogs fattened on mast or peanuts.

Virginia hams and bacon soon became noted for their excellence all over the world. The fame of these products has never waned. Unfortunately, most hotels and restaurants in the United State now use the term "Virginia ham" on their menus to designate this sort of meat regardless of its origin or cure. New England ships, plying a coastwise traffic with the Caribbean countries, frequently stopped in Jamestown for cargoes of salted meats. This trade was especially desirable during times when the price of tobacco fell to ruinous levels. Most of the hogs ran wild. Some planters marked their animals by ear-cuts, and then could claim an entire drove, if they had a number of their branded hogs in it.

CATTLE

Neat animals were kept near Jamestown in the early years, but they, like the swine, had to gather their own living. A few were trained for draft purposes. In new grounds where stumps and roots prevail, oxen are more useful than horses. They do not get in a panic when obstacles interfere. Then too, they can be slaughtered for beef when they become too old for work. During the period under study, cattle, in Virginia, often brought good prices. Many were purchased by the New England colonists as it was cheaper to buy animals, in America, than to go to the expense and loss of animals by shipping them across the ocean.

There was a market for oxen in the Caribbean region, where they were used for power, in the sugar mills.

In the first thirty years, some of the cattle went wild in the back country, but many of the cows were kept in the vicinity of the Jamestown headquarters. While not notable as dairy cows, they produced enough milk so that Virginia gained a reputation among ship crews for its excellent butter and cheese. In 1649 it was estimated that there were twenty thousand cattle in the Colony.

GOATS AND SHEEP

Flocks of goats and sheep became noticeable to visitors about the middle of the century. Many were brought to Virginia. In the early years the numbers killed by wolves made them unprofitable. Heavy bounties paid for wolf heads eventually reduced the depredations of this predator until sheep and goats were fairly safe. As producers of meat and wool for clothing sheep contributed to the general welfare of the colony. By 1649, the number of sheep was estimated at three thousand; and of goats at five thousand.

HORSES

Of all the domestic animals brought from England to Jamestown in the early days of the settlement, the most expensive to transport and the most useless after they arrived in Virginia were horses. The estimate of the number in the Colony in 1649 is 200. There was no purpose for them to serve. The fragile wooden plows of the seventeenth century were of no use among the stumps and roots in newly cleared forest lands. Horses were of no value for transportation as there were no roads through the forests or bridges over the rivers. They were of little use as beasts of burden as there were few burdens to carry. A horse was no match for an able-bodied man on Indian trails through timbered country. As late as 1671, the Batts and Fallam expedition, consisting of five white men and seven Indians, who were the discoverers of New River, had horses for the white men when they left Petersburg. All of these animals were dead before they reached the mountains.

The colonists did all they could afford to do with the horses brought to them and that was to turn them loose to shift for themselves. In a very few years there was a band of wild horses roaming the woods in the back country. Eventually these wild horses provided a great deal of recreation for the younger planters. Capturing and breaking to the saddle wild horses became a popular sport. As soon as a horse was caught and accustomed to a rider the most natural thing was to try it for speed.

Horse-racing began with local contests but developed into a major sport. King Charles II is credited with having imported Turk and Arabian horses to England. Some of this blooded stock may have been shipped to Jamestown. At any rate Virginia saddle-horses at an early date began to attract attention because of their speed.

Two other colonies, Rhode Island and New York were famous for their fast horses. Racing became an inter-colonial sport. The first regular race course was the New Market on Hempstead Plains, Long Island. There the fleetest horses of Long Island were brought together to settle all arguments by actual trial. This famous race course was described in 1670 by a contemporary, Daniel Denton: "Toward the middle of Long Island lyeth a plain sixteen miles long and four broad, upon which plain grows very fine grass, that makes exceeding good hay, and is very good pasture for sheep or other cattel; where you shall find neither stick nor stone to hinder the horse heels or endanger them in their races, and once a year the best horses in the island are brought hither to try their swiftness, and the swiftest rewarded with a silver cup, two being annually procured for that purpose."

Horse-racing became of economic importance to these colonies. The sugar planters, in the Caribbean region, also became interested in this "sport of kings" and sent agents to buy the fastest horses they could find. High prices were sometimes paid for prize winning animals.

Governor Francis Nicholson in 1690, "gave prizes to those that should excell in riding, running, wrestling and cudgeling." Of these sports, riding became by far the most popular. Interest in horse-racing, fox-chasing, steeple-chasing, and riding tournaments has never entirely died out in Virginia.

CONCLUSION

A great deal has been written about the events that occurred during the ninety-two years that elapsed, from the settlement of the colony on Jamestown Island, and the change of capital site to Williamsburg. Judging from the recorded observations of visitors during that period, no great difference in the general appearance of the landscape had taken place. It still looked very much like a wilderness. Much forest land had been cleared, farmed for a few years, and then turned back to nature. The mammoth trees with scanty undergrowth, that the firstcomers found, had been replaced with a luxuriant second or third growth. If the top-soil is not eroded away a new forest can be produced in Virginia in thirty or forty years.

One of the most noticeable improvements was in the dwelling houses. Substantial brick and frame buildings had replaced the hurriedly constructed shacks of the early days.

The accumulated wealth from the surplus products resulting from their farming activities was reflected in their flocks and herds of horses, cattle, sheep, goats, swine, and poultry. Dire famine no longer stared them in face. Through insistence that only the best quality products should be shipped abroad, favorable trade relations had been established in the commerce of the world.

Perhaps the greatest achievement of all was the creation of the farm home where a family could own, in fee simple, the land they tilled, live in peace, and enjoy the fruits of their own labor.

BIBLIOGRAPHY

1. Beverley, Robert. *History of Virginia* . . . Reprinted from the author's 2nd. rev. ed., London, 1722. Richmond, Virginia, 1855.

2. Brown, Alexander. *The Genesis of the United States.* Boston and New York, 1890. 2 Vols.

3. Bruce, P. A. *Economic History of Virginia in the Seventeenth Century.* New York, 1895. 2 Vols.

4. Bullock, William. *Virginia Impartially Examined* . . . London, 1649.

5. Campbell, Charles. *History of the Colony and Ancient Dominion of Virginia* . . . Philadelphia, 1860.

6. Clayton, Rev. John. *A letter* . . . *May 12, 1688. Giving an Account of Several Observables in Virginia* . . . Reprint in Force, Peter. Tracts . . . Washington, 1836-46. Vol. 3.

7. Devries, David Peterson. *Voyages from Holland to America.* New York, 1853.

8. Force, Peter. *Tracts and Other Papers,* Relating Principally to the Origin, Settlement, and Progress of the Colonies of North America. Washington. 4 Vols.

   Gray, Lewis C. History of Agriculture in the Southern United States to 1860. Washington, D. C. 2 Vols.

9. Hakluyt, Richard. *Collection of Early Voyages, Travels and Discoveries of the English Nation.* London, 1809-12. 5 Vols. Also Edinburgh, 1885-90. 16 Vols.

10. Hamor, Ralph. *A True Discourse of the Present State of Virginia* . . . London, 1615. Albany, J. Munsell, 1860.

11. Hariot, Thomas. *Narrative of the First English Plantation of Virginia.* London, 1588. Reproduced after DeBry's illustrated edition printed in Frankfort in 1590, the illustrations having been designed in Virginia in 1585 by John White. London, B. Quaritch, 1893.

12. Hening, W. W. *Virginia Statutes at Large,* 1619-1792. 13 Vols.

13. Jefferson, Thomas. *Notes on the State of Virginia.* Richmond, J. W. Randolph, 1853.

14. Purchas, Samuel. *Purchas his Pilgrims.* London, 1626. 5 Vols.

15. Smith, Captain John. *Works.* Edited by Arber, 1884. Also Edinburgh 1910. 2 Vols.

16. Spotswood, Alexander. *Official Letters,* 1710-1722. Ed. by R. A. Brock. Virginia Historical Society Collections. Richmond, 1882-85. 2 Vols.

17. Strachey, William. *The Historie of Travaile Into Virginia Britannia* . . . London. Printed for the Hakluyt Society, 1849.

18. Swem, E. G. *Virginia Historical Index.* Roanoke, Virginia. 1934-36. 2 Vols.

19. *Virginia Company of London. Abstract of the Proceedings of the Company* . . . *1619-1624.* By Conway Robinson. Edited by R. A. Brock. Virginia Historical Society, 1888-89.

20. *Virginia Truly Valued.* In Force's *Tracts,* Vol. 3.

APPENDIX I

A PLOWMAN'S DAY

This is an extract from Markham's *Farewell to Husbandry, or the Enriching of all Sorts of barren and Steril grounds in our Kingdome,* a well-known book on farming as carried on in England in the early years of the 17th century; it is presented here in order to show what the daily tasks of a farmer were at that time, and what might be expected, according to this standard, of a settler coming to Virginia. The author, Gervase Markham, issued several editions of the work. This extract is from the fourth edition, printed in 1638, of which a title-page is reproduced in this booklet, from the copy in the William and Mary College Library. Markham's book has an additional interest, for the reason that in the supplies sent by ship *Supply* in 1620 to Berkeley Hundred, a copy of the current edition was included.

Having thus generally runne over (in a short computation) the labours of the husbandman, I will now briefly as I can, goe over the particular daies labours of a farmer or plowman, shewing the particular expence of every houre of the day, from his first rising, till his going to bed, as thus for example: We will suppose it to be after Christmas, and about plow-day (which is the first letting out of the plough) and at what time men either begin to fallow, or to break up pease earth, which is to lie to bait, according to the custome of the country; at this time the plough-man shall rise before foure of the clocke in the morning, and after thankes given to God for his rest, and the successe of his labours he shall go into his stable, or beaste-house, and first he shall fodder his cattell, then cleanse the house, and make the booths cleane, rub downe the cattell, and cleanse their skins of all filth, then he shall curry his horses, rub them with clothes and wisps, and make both them and the stable as cleane as may be, then he shall water both his oxen and horses, and housing them againe, give them more fodder, and to his horse by all meanes provender, as chaffe and dry pease or beanes, or oat-hulls, pease or beanes or cleane oates, or clean garbage (which is the hinder ends of any kinde of graine but rye) with the straw chop'd small amongst it, according as the ability of the husbandman is. And whilst they are eating their meat, he shall make ready his collars, hames, treats, halters, mullens, and plough-geares, seeing everything fit, and in his due place, and to these labours I will also allow full two houres, that is, from foure of the clocke till sixe, then hee shall come in to breakfast, and to that

MARKHAMS

Farewell to

HVSBANDRY:

OR,

The Enriching of all forts of Barren and
Steril grounds in our Kingdome, to be as
fruitfull in all manner of Graine, Pulfe, and
Graffe, as the beft grounds whatfoever.

Together with the annoyances, and preservation of all
Graine and Seed, from one yeare to many yeares.

As alfo a Husbandly computation of men and Cattels
daily labours, their expeences, charges, and utmoft profits.

The fourth time, revifed, corrected, and amended, together with
many new Additions, and cheape experiments:

For the bettering of arable Pafture, and wooddy Grounds. Of
making good all grounds againe, fpoiled with overflowing of fale
water by Sea-breaches: as alfo, the Enriching of the Hop-garden;
and many other things never publifhed before.

LONDON,

Printed by EDVVARD GRIFFIN for IOHN HARISON,
at the figne of the golden Vnicorne in Pater-nofter-
row. 1638.

38

I allow him halfe an houre; and then another halfe houre to the gearing and yoaking of his cattell, so that at seven of the clocke hee may set forward to his labour, and then he shall plow from seven of the clock in the morning, till betwixt two and three in the afternoone, then he shall unyoke, and bring home his cattell, and having rubb'd them, drest them, and cleansed away all durt and filth, he shall fodder them, and give them meate, then shall the servants goe in to their dinner, which allowed halfe an houre; it will then be towards foure of the clocke, at what time hee shall goe to his cattell againe, and rubbing them downe, and cleansing their stalls, give them more fodder, which done, he shall go into the barnes, and provide and make ready fodder of all kinds for the next day, whether it be hay, straw, or blend fodder, according to the ability of the husbandman: this being done, and carried into the stable, oxe-house, or other convenient place, he shall then goe water his cattell, and give them more meate, and to his horse provender, as before shewed; and by this time it will draw past sixe of the clocke, at which time he shall come in to supper, and after supper, he shall either by the fire side, mend shooes both for himselfe and their family, or beat and knock hemp, or flaxe, or picke and stampe apples, or crabs for cider or verdjuce, or else grind malt on the quernes, picke candle rushes, or do some husbandly office within dores, till it be full eight a clocke: then shall he take his lanthorne and candle, and goe to his cattell, and having cleansed the stalls and plankes, litter them downe, looke that they be safely tied, and then fodder and give them meate for all night, then giving God thankes for benefits received that day, let him and the whole houshold goe to their rest till the next morning.

Now it may be intended, that there may be in the houshold more servants than one; and so you will demand of mee, what the rest of the servants shall be imployed in before and after the time of plowing: to this I answer, that they may either goe into the barne and thrash, fill or empty the maltfat, load and unload the kilne, or any other good and necessary work that is about the yard, and after they come from plowing, some may goe into the barne and thrash, some hedge, ditch, stop gaps in broken fences, dig in the orchard or garden, or any other out-worke which is needfull to be done, and which about the husband-man is never wanting, especially one must have a care every night to looke to the mending or sharpening of the plough-irons, and the repairing of the plough and plough-geares, if any be out of order, for to deferre them till the morrow, were the losse of a daies worke, and an ill point of husbandry.

APPENDIX II

In the early years at Jamestown, much grain was shipped from England for the use of the colonists. The extract, which follows, is from Markham's *Farewell to Husbandry*, 4th edition, 1638. The term "corn" as used by Markham does not mean maize (Indian corn), but wheat, barley, rye, or oats.

And first for transportation of graine by sea, it is two waies to be done, as either in great quantities for trade and the victuallyng of other nations, or in smaller quantity for victualling the men in the ship, prepared for a long and tedious voyage.

For the transporting of graine for trade in great quantities, it is to be intended the voyage is seldom long, but from neighbor to neighbor, and therefore commonly they make close decks in the ships to receive the graine, faire and even boorded, yet if such decks be matted and lined both under and on each side, it is much the better, and this matting would be strong and thinne; there bee some which make the decks only of mats, and sure it is sweet, but not so strong as the boord, therefore the best way of transportation is to have strong boorded deckes well matted, and then spreading the corne of a reasonable thicknesse, to cover it with matting againe, and then to lay corne on it againe, and then mats againe, that betweene every reasonable thicknesse of graine a mat may lie, the profit whereof is, that when the corne with his owne heate and the working of the sea shall beginne to sweate, which sweat for want of aire to drie it up, would turne to putrifaction, then the mats thus lying betweene, will not only exhale and sucke up the sweate, but also keep the corne so coole and dry, that no imperfection shall come unto it: and here is to be noted, that these mats should rather be made of dry white bents, than of flagges and bulrush, for the bent is a firme, dry, crispe thing, and will not relent or sweat of it selfe, but the flag or bulrush is a spungy and soft substance which is never empty of his own and other moystures.

Now for transporting of graine, for victualls for the ship, which is in much smaller quantity, because it is best for the private use of a few within the ship; the only best and safest way, is, to take salt-fish barrells, or any caske in which any salt-fish hath beene piled, as cod, herrings, salmon, sprats, or any other powdred *[i.e., salted]* fish; and whilest the vessels are sweet, you shall calke them both, within and without, plaster [and] daubing them all over; then into them put your graine of what kinde soever it be, and head them up close, and then stow them in such convenient dry place of the ship, as you shall thinke fit; and questionlesse, if beliefe may be given to the worthiest authors, which hath writ in this kinde, you may thus keepe your graine sweet, sound and in full perfection from one yeere to an hundred and twenty yeers; but certainly daily experience shows us, that all kind of graine thus put up and kept, will remaine sound and sweet, three, foure, and as some say, seven yeeres, for so far hath lately been try'd; and what here I speake of [on] ship-boord, the like may be done in any town of war or garrison, whether besieged, or not besieged, or in any other place, where any necessity shall compell; the proofe of this manner of piling or putting up of graine, serveth as well for land as sea.